ADVENTURES OF SU

MW01037548

EAT IN PEACE

SIR, IS RICE GROWN IN FIELDS?

YES.

AND, PULSES?

YES. PULSES TOO.

SIR, CAN YOU COME HERE AND TELL ME IF THE WHEAT IS DRY ENOUGH?

SUPPANDI, LET ME EAT IN PEACE! YOU MUST NEVER DISTURB ANYONE WHO'S EATING.

A FEW DAYS LATER –

SUPPANDI, WHAT ARE YOU DOING?

THAT GOAT IS EATING OUR CUCUMBERS! WHY DON'T YOU DRIVE IT AWAY?

IT'S EATING, SIR! DIDN'T YOU TELL ME NOT TO DISTURB ANYONE WHILE THEY ARE EATING?

AWK!

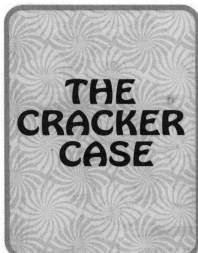

THE CRACKER CASE

SUPPANDI'S EMPLOYER WAS A GROCER.

SIR, WHY DO YOU KEEP ALL YOUR MONEY IN THAT ALMIRAH?

MONEY SHOULD BE KEPT IN A SAFE PLACE, AND THIS ALMIRAH IS A VERY SAFE PLACE INDEED!

A FEW WEEKS LATER –

HAPPY DIWALI!

HAPPY DIWALI!

SUPPANDI, TAKE THESE CRACKERS AND HELP THE CHILDREN BURST THEM. FOLLOW THE INSTRUCTIONS ON THE PACKET.

SUDDENLY –

BANG BANG BANG

SUPPANDI...(GAK!)...(COUGH!)... WHY DID YOU BURST...(COUGH!)... THE CRACKERS INSIDE THE ALMIRAH?

COUGH

COUGH

BECAUSE!...(COUGH!)...THE PACKET SAID THAT ...(COUGH!)...THE CRACKERS HAD TO BE BURST!...(COUGH!)... IN A SAFE PLACE.

AAAARGH!

FARE ENOUGH

SUPPANDI, GO, DELIVER THIS PARCEL TO MY BROTHER AT HIS OFFICE!

VERY WELL, SIR.

AND HERE'S 20 RUPEES FOR THE AUTORICKSHAW.

OKAY, SIR!

AND SOON –

HERE WE ARE. THAT WILL BE 25 RUPEES.

BUT I'VE GOT ONLY 20 RUPEES.

YOU HAD BETTER TAKE OUT ANOTHER FIVE RUPEES OR ELSE…!

THERE'S NO NEED TO GET ANGRY.

JUST REVERSE TILL THE METER COMES DOWN TO 20 RUPEES!

PICK POCKET

NO TALKING

SUPPANDI'S NEW EMPLOYER WAS A DOCTOR. ONE DAY –

SIR, ...(CHOMP)... WILL YOU BE...(CHOMP)... GOING TO THE...(CHOMP)... CLINIC TODAY?

SUPPANDI, ONE MUST NEVER SPEAK WHILE EATING. IT'S BAD MANNERS AND NOT GOOD FOR DIGESTION.

YES SIR.

ONE AFTERNOON SUPPANDI'S EMPLOYER CALLED HOME...

...BUT SUPPANDI DIDN'T ANSWER THE PHONE.

IN THE EVENING, WHEN SUPPANDI'S EMPLOYER RETURNED –

SUPPANDI, I CALLED HOME THIS AFTERNOON BUT YOU DIDN'T ANSWER THE PHONE. DID YOU GO OUT?

I WAS AT HOME, SIR. BUT I WAS HAVING MY LUNCH.

... AND YOU SAID ONE MUST NEVER TALK WHILE EATING. SO I DID NOT PICK UP THE PHONE.

!?!

NO VALUE

SUPPANDI'S EMPLOYER WAS A MATHS TEACHER.

HOW MUCH IS 0 + 0 AND 0 – 0, SIR?

WHETHER YOU ADD OR SUBTRACT, THE ANSWER WOULD STILL BE ZERO…

… AS ZERO HAS NO VALUE.

OH, I SEE!

ONE DAY, AFTER SUPPANDI RETURNED FROM THE MARKET –

YOU'VE NOT ACCOUNTED FOR ALL THE MONEY I GAVE YOU, SUPPANDI. NINETY NINE RUPEES ARE MISSING.

OH, THAT! I HAD TO GIVE ONE RUPEE TO A SHOPKEEPER AND I DIDN'T HAVE A SINGLE COIN. FORTUNATELY I REMEMBERED WHAT YOU SAID ABOUT ZERO HAVING NO VALUE…

I CANCELLED TWO ZEROES FROM A HUNDRED RUPEE NOTE AND GAVE IT TO HIM AS ONE RUPEE.

TOO REMOTE

LOOK AT THIS REMOTE CONTROL, SUPPANDI…

… I CAN STAND IN THE KITCHEN AND CHANGE CHANNELS.

THAT EVENING WHEN SUPPANDI'S EMPLOYER RETURNED FROM WORK –

SO, DID YOU WATCH T.V.? ISN'T THE SET WONDERFUL?

THAT IT IS, SIR, BUT CHANGING CHANNELS IS A NUISANCE.

WHY?

ONE HAS TO GO TO THE KITCHEN EACH TIME.

OOERGH!

SAVING TIME

ONE DAY, SUPPANDI'S EMPLOYER BOUGHT SOME APPLES AND A HUGE QUANTITY OF ORANGES.

THE APPLES AND THE ORANGES HAVE GOT MIXED UP. SUPPANDI, YOU'LL HAVE TO SEPARATE THEM.

NO PROBLEM, SIR!

AND SO –

PICK OUT THE APPLES. SINCE THEY ARE FEWER YOU'LL SAVE TIME.

YES, SIR!

A FEW DAYS LATER –

THE GARDEN IS FULL OF WEEDS. PULL THEM OUT, WILL YOU.

HEY, WHY HAVE YOU REMOVED THE PLANTS, YOU IDIOT!

THE PLANTS ARE FEW, AND THE WEEDS MANY...

THIS WAY THE JOB WILL GET DONE FASTER!

9

CONSIDERATE WRITER

SO HAS SUPPANDI DONE ANYTHING STUPID RECENTLY?

NO... FOR A CHANGE.

WHAT IS HE DOING RIGHT NOW?

HE HAS BEEN WRITING A LETTER FOR THE PAST ONE HOUR.

REALLY? HE MUST BE TURNING INTELLIGENT. I MUST SEE THE LETTER.

SURE! SUPPANDI, BRING THAT LETTER YOU'RE WRITING.

SUPPANDI CAME AND SHOWED THE LETTER —

WHAT!? ONLY FIVE LINES IN THE PAST HOUR. WHY ARE YOU WRITING SO SLOWLY?

WELL, SIR, MY COUSIN READS VERY SLOWLY AND IT WOULD BE VERY DIFFICULT FOR HIM TO READ...

...IF I WROTE THE LETTER ANY FASTER.

Like everybody else I too have my favourite toons...
... the DUMBBELLS!

The **Dumbbells** Nattoo, Dattoo and Motu as their collective name suggests, are not the brightest of guys but they're an adventurous trio, and their escapades and blunders leave you in splits.

The brainchild of Prasad Iyer, former associate editor of Tinkle, the **DUMBBELLS** made its debut in Tinkle 133 published in July 1987, and ran for several months, delighting readers of all ages.

It was illustrated by Anand Mande whose sudden departure for greener pastures in 1990 brought a sudden end to the series, much to the disappointment of its numerous fans.

THE DUMBBELLS IN TROUBLE

13

GOOD NUTRITION

SUPPANDI'S NEW EMPLOYER WAS A HEALTH FREAK.

ONE, TWO, THREE... HUP, TWO, THREE, FOUR...

SUPPANDI, IT IS VERY IMPORTANT TO TAKE CARE OF YOUR BODY. PLENTY OF EXERCISE AND NUTRITIOUS FOOD IS A MUST.

YES, SIR.

YOU MUST MAKE SURE THAT THE FOOD YOU SERVE ME IS RICH IN VITAMINS.

YES, SIR.

A FEW DAYS LATER AT LUNCH TIME –

SIR, THE COOKING OIL WAS OVER...

GAK! ARE YOU TRYING TO POISON ME? WHAT KIND OF OIL DID YOU USE IN THIS FOOD?!

... SO I USED THIS VITAMIN-E-ENRICHED HAIR OIL INSTEAD.

GURK!

17

MEAL MANNERS

ONE DAY WHEN SUPPANDI'S EMPLOYER HAD VISITORS –

CHOMP CHOMP CHOMP

LATER – SUPPANDI, YOU SHOULD NEVER EAT IN FRONT OF VISITORS. IT'S BAD MANNERS.

ALL RIGHT, SIR.

A FEW DAYS LATER WHEN THERE WERE GUESTS AT THE HOUSE AGAIN —

CHOMP CHOMP

WHAT ARE YOU DOING SUPPANDI?

SIR, YOU ASKED ME NEVER TO EAT IN FRONT OF GUESTS…

…SO I'M STANDING BEHIND THEM AND EATING.

EEP!

ANTI ANTS

SIR, WHY ARE YOU SPRINKLING CHALK POWDER ON THE FLOOR?

IT'S NOT CHALK POWDER, SUPPANDI...

...IT IS A PESTICIDE. IT KEEPS ANTS AWAY.

I SEE.

THE NEXT DAY –

SUPPANDI, I'M EXPECTING A GUEST. COVER THESE SWEETS AND SEE THAT THE ANTS DON'T GET TO THEM.

DON'T WORRY, SIR.

WHEN THE GUEST ARRIVED –

AHA! SWEETS WITH GRATED COCONUT! JUST WHAT I LOVE.

SUPPANDI MUST HAVE THOUGHT OF PUTTING THE COCONUT.

NO, SIR, ALL I PUT OVER THE SWEETS WAS THE PESTICIDE TO KEEP THE ANTS AWAY.

YECH!

SUPPANDI FOLLOWS INSTRUCTIONS

WE'RE GOING TO BORPUR, SUPPANDI. BRING ME MY SHOES.

YES, SIR.

HERE YOU ARE, SIR.

YOU FOOL! I ASKED YOU TO FETCH ME MY SHOES AND YOU BRING ME CHAPPALS!!

CAN'T YOU FOLLOW SIMPLE INSTRUCTIONS?

HUH! ISN'T HE FUSSY?

SOON —

URK!

HELP!

WRONG CUE

SUPPANDI WAS WASHING THE PLATES ONE DAY WHEN –

CRASH

I BROKE A PLATE, SIR.

FIX IT WITH GLUE SUPPANDI.

A FEW DAYS LATER –

SUPPANDI, LET US GO AND SEE CHINNA PLAY THE ROLE OF ABHIMANYU IN HIS SCHOOL PLAY.

YES, SIR.

IN THE PLAY –

OH! KARNA HAS BROKEN MY BOW.

DON'T WORRY, CHINNA…

…YOU CAN FIX IT WITH GLUE.

HA! HA! HA!

SHEESH!

HA! HA!

TOTAL WASHOUT

THAT SHIRT LOOKS SOILED. DIDN'T YOU WASH IT?

I DID! BUT WHILE I WAS TAKING IT TO THE SHOP FOR IRONING I DROPPED IT ON THE GROUND!

YOU WILL HAVE TO WASH IT AGAIN!

AGAIN, SIR?

I'M A STICKLER FOR CLEANLINESS. SO ANYTHING THAT FALLS ON THE GROUND HAS TO BE WASHED WITH SOAP AND WATER.

I'LL REMEMBER THAT!

THE NEXT MORNING –
SIR, HERE IS YOUR NEWSPAPER.

YES! BUT WHY IS IT SOAKING WET, YOU IDIOT?

WHILE I WAS BRINGING IT TO YOU I DROPPED IT ON THE GROUND…

…BUT I REMEMBERED YOUR INSTRUCTIONS AND WASHED IT THOROUGHLY WITH SOAP AND WATER.

23

FLY IN SOUP

SUPPANDI'S EMPLOYER HAD INVITED HIS FRIEND, VIJU FOR DINNER.

DING DONG

HERE HE IS, SUPPANDI! SEE THAT EVERYTHING GOES WELL.

YES, SIR.

WELCOME, VIJU.

AFTER SOME TIME –

VIJU, ARE YOU READY FOR DINNER?

YES.

SUPPANDI, SERVE THE SOUP!

YES, SIR.

SUPPANDI, A FLY HAS FALLEN INTO THE SOUP!

DON'T LET IT BOTHER YOU, SIR!

AFTER ALL, HOW MUCH SOUP CAN A FLY CONSUME?

KEY TO THE SITUATION

ONE MORNING –

THE SUITCASE IN WHICH I HAD KEPT THE MONEY I HAD WITHDRAWN FROM THE BANK HAS BEEN STOLEN.

AND NO ONE SAW THE BURGLARS!

NO, SIR. NOT BURGLARS! THERE WAS ONLY ONE BURGLAR.

DID YOU SEE HIM?

BUT, OF COURSE!

THEN WHY DIDN'T YOU YELL OR WAKE ME UP?

I WAS ABOUT TO DO THAT!

THEN I GOT A BRAINWAVE!

WHAT DID YOU DO?

I HID THE KEY OF THE SUITCASE.

TICK TOCK

SUPPANDI, THE CLOCK HAS STOPPED.

SOMETHING'S WRONG WITH IT. I WILL TAKE IT TO THE WATCH REPAIRER.

YOU DO THAT. SEE THAT IT'S WORKING BY THE TIME I RETURN.

I'LL GO RIGHT AWAY.

BUT –

OOF! IT IS HEAVY!

WHAT! YOU HAVE BROUGHT ONLY THE PENDULUM?

BUT OF COURSE! THIS IS THE ONLY PART THAT IS NOT WORKING.

26

THE BEST COMPANION

I had just returned to Mumbai from Chennai and i was telling my friends about my stay there. W
When i told them that the first friend i made there was a boy named vissu, all of them became very excited. "
Was he cute?" asked one. "
Handsome?" asked another. "
Oh, he was very cute, hand-some and so fair," i answered, a wistful expression on my face. "
He was the best companion anybody could every have wished for". T
here was a moment's silence. "
How old is he?" asked one of the girls finally. "
Two years", I answered and all of them burst into loud laughter.

A true-life incident sent by:
miss vinita manocha
New delhi – 110024

THE FRUIT THIEF

My house has a neat little garden with a beautiful marble statue in the centre. There are also several trees that are often laden with fruit. Quite naturally, they attract the attention of mischief-makers. One of them stole fruits every day and it annoyed me so much that i decided to catch the thief all by myself.
o one night, after dinner, I waited in the garden behind a big tree. It was a moonless night and it was quite dark. Suddenly i thought i heard the footsteps of the thief. I did not want the thief to get away so i rushed forward, grabbed him and shouted: "thief ! Thief !" my parents and some of our neighbours ame running out with torches. They stopped and then roared with laughter. I was surprised at their behaviour but I soon knew why -- I had flung my arms around he marble statue!
A

A true-life incident sent by: puspen karmarkar
Dist. Burdwan, West bengal.

27

IT HAPPENED TO ME

HAIR FOR GRANDPA

When I was very young, I spent a holiday in Goa with my grandparents. My grandpa was bald and had hair only at the sides. One day my mother took me to a saloon for a haircut. The saloon was crowded and we had to wait for my turn. When I looked around I saw a lot of hair on the ground. I started picking it up and putting it in my pocket. A barber asked me why I was doing so. I told him that I was going to stick it with glue on my grandpa's pate. Everyone in the saloon laughed.

Based on a true-life
Incident sent by:
Rajesh Poddar,
Mumbai – 400 058.

SLIPPERY CHARACTER

One morning, I was strolling along the corridors of the fifth floor of my building, when I saw the milkman. He had kept his slippers in between the lift doors to keep them from closing. I knew then why my mother had a problem in getting the lift every morning. For his own convenience, the milkman had been depriving others of the facility of the lift. I removed the slippers to let the doors of the automatic elevator shut. When the milkman heard the doors shut with a bang, he came running and found his slippers lying at some distance away from the lift. I told him the lift doors had thrown the slippers away and next time they would cut the slippers into two, now that the lift had been computerised.

Thereafter, he never left his slippers between the lift doors.

Based on a true-life incident sent by:
Vinod Chandrachoodan,
Mumbai – 400 094.

BOTH INCIDENTS ON THIS PAGE HAVE BEEN TAKEN FROM TINKLE ARCHIVES.

MAGIC TRICK

ONCE SUPPANDI AND HIS EMPLOYER WERE TRAVELLING BY TRAIN.

IT'S GETTING SO BORING! I'LL HAVE SOME FUN WITH SUPPANDI!

I'LL SHOW YOU A MAGIC TRICK, SUPPANDI.

SEE THIS PAPER CUP IN MY HAND... NOW I'LL THROW IT OUT OF THE WINDOW!

NO! NO! WE'LL LOSE THE CUP!

HEH HEH! OF COURSE NOT!

I'LL GET IT BACK AGAIN.

ABRACADABRA!

HERE! HA! HA!

SIR, YOU ARE GREAT!

IT WAS SO EASY TO TRICK HIM! HE DIDN'T KNOW I HAD ANOTHER CUP HIDDEN BEHIND MY BACK.

LET ME TRY! I'LL THROW YOUR WALLET OUT...

HEH HEH! HE HAS THROWN OUT MY WALLET... SO HE SAYS. HEH HEH!

OH, NO! SUPPANDI, YOU DIDN'T REALLY THROW MY WALLET OUT, DID YOU?

OF COURSE, I THREW IT OUT. NOW, SIR, PLEASE SHOW ME HOW TO GET IT BACK.

SUPPANDI THE CAREFUL

SUPPANDI, I'VE GOT EIGHTY FIVE PER CENT IN MY S.S.C. EXAMS!

WONDERFUL!

SUPPANDI, GO AND GET TEN PHOTOCOPIES OF THIS MARKSHEET, WE HAVE TO LEAVE RIGHT AWAY.

YES, SIR!

SUPPANDI DASHED OFF BUT DID NOT RETURN EVEN AFTER AN HOUR –

CAN'T WASTE ANY MORE TIME WAITING. LET'S GO TO THE SHOP.

YES, FATHER! LET'S HURRY.

AH, THERE HE IS, STARING AT THE PHOTOCOPIES! THE IDIOT!

WHAT ARE YOU DOING HERE, SUPPANDI?

I AM CHECKING TO MAKE SURE THE MARKS PRINTED ON THE PHOTOCOPIES ARE THE SAME AS THOSE IN THE MARKSHEET, SIR.

SUPPANDI MAILS A COAT

SUPPANDI'S EMPLOYER HAD GONE TO STAY WITH HIS SON IN THE CITY. HE HAD FORGOTTEN HIS FAVOURITE COAT AT HOME AND HAD WRITTEN TO SUPPANDI TO POST IT TO HIM.

I HOPE IT ARRIVES IN TIME FOR OUR SON'S WEDDING ANNIVERSARY.

IT SHOULD.

TWO DAYS LATER –

PARCEL FOR YOU, GRANDPA.

IT MUST BE MY COAT.

SO SUPPANDI CAN BE DEPENDED UPON, AFTER ALL...

EH, WHAT'S THIS! ALL THE BUTTONS ON THE COAT ARE MISSING...

... THERE IS A NOTE HERE.

IT IS FROM SUPPANDI. HE WRITES: I HAVE CUT OFF THE BUTTONS IN ORDER TO REDUCE THE WEIGHT OF THE COAT...SO IT'LL COST LESS TO SEND.

OH NO! NOW I'LL HAVE TO BUY BUTTONS THAT MATCH YOUR COAT AND SEW THEM ON.

NO, YOU WON'T HAVE TO DO THAT. OUR GENIUS HAS WRITTEN A POST-SCRIPT.

HE SAYS HE HAS PUT THE BUTTONS IN THE POCKET.

FASTER ON FOOT

ONE MORNING WHEN SUPPANDI RETURNED FROM AN ERRAND —

SUPPANDI, YOU FORGOT TO BRING MY CLOTHES FROM THE LAUNDRY!

I'LL GO RIGHT BACK AND GET THEM!

TAKE THE BICYCLE AND GET THERE QUICKLY OR I'LL BE LATE TO THE OFFICE.

THE BICYCLE?! UH…OKAY…!

AN HOUR PASSED —

I WONDER WHY HE IS TAKING SO LONG.

IT'S ALREADY PAST NINE!

SIR, I AM BACK.

WHERE DID YOU GO? ON A WORLD TOUR? IT TAKES HARDLY TEN MINUTES BY CYCLE TO THE LAUNDRY AND BACK!

IT'S THE CYCLE THAT DELAYED ME.

AS I DON'T KNOW HOW TO RIDE IT, I HAD TO WHEEL IT ALL THE WAY TO THE SHOP AND BACK!

SUPPANDI SAVES WATER

THERE WAS A WATER SHORTAGE AND SUPPANDI'S EMPLOYER HAD INSTRUCTED HIM TO GET UP EARLY AND STORE WATER FOR THE DAY –

THERE! THAT'S DONE...

TWO HOURS LATER –

EEEEE!

WHAT HAPPENED?

SEE!

SEE WHAT HE HAS DONE! HE HAS FILLED THE FLOUR BIN WITH WATER!

WHY DID YOU DO SUCH A THING, SUPPANDI?

SHE ADDS WATER TO THE FLOUR EVERY TIME SHE MAKES CHAPPATIS.

AND SOMETIMES THERE IS NO WATER... I THOUGHT I WOULD WET THE FLOUR ONCE AND FOR ALL.

YOU... YOU...

SPLOT

SHE'S ENVIOUS BECAUSE THE IDEA DIDN'T OCCUR TO HER...

...OH, THESE WOMEN!

NO PROBLEM

HALF A TEASPOON

POST SCRIPT

ONE DAY –

SIR, WILL YOU WRITE A LETTER FOR ME?

RIGHT AWAY? UH... WELL OKAY!

AND SO –

BLAH! BLAH! BLAH!

BLAH! BLAH! BLAH!

BLAH! BLAH! BLAH!

I HAVE NEVER WRITTEN SUCH A LONG LETTER IN MY LIFE!

NEVER MIND! IT'S NOT EVERY DAY THAT SUPPANDI ASKS ME TO WRITE A LETTER.

...AND GIVE MY REGARDS TO YOUR PARENTS. YOUR FRIEND, SUPPANDI. THAT'S ALL!

(PHEW!) IT'S OVER!

SIR! THERE'S ONE THING I COMPLETELY FORGOT. COULD IT BE ADDED NOW?

OH, YES.

ASK HIM TO SEND ME HIS ADDRESS AS SOON AS POSSIBLE!

NEW FROM OLD

* A SAVOURY SNACK.

ALWAYS CHECK FOR DEFECTS

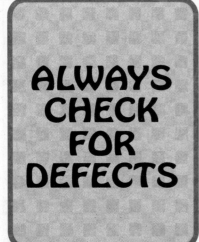

ONCE SUPPANDI WENT SHOPPING WITH HIS NEW EMPLOYER.

MADAM, I TOO WOULD LIKE TO BUY A SAREE FOR MY MOTHER.

SURE, SUPPANDI!

I'LL TAKE THIS ONE.

SUPPANDI, BEFORE YOU BUY ANYTHING, ALWAYS CHECK FOR DEFECTS BY OPENING IT, LIKE THIS.

LATER –

SUPPANDI, BUY ME A ROLL OF FILM FOR MY CAMERA, PLEASE.

DID YOU GET IT, SUPPANDI?

YES, I DID MADAM, AND DON'T WORRY, IT'S NOT DEFECTIVE…

…I HAVE OPENED IT AND CHECKED IT.

AARRGH!

THE DUMBBELLS SCORE A VICTORY

41

SAFER PLACE

SUPPANDI WAS AT THE RAILWAY STATION WITH HIS EMPLOYER.

JUST THEN –

YOUR ATTENTION PLEASE. THE 3210 DOWN CHENNAI EXPRESS WILL BE ARRIVING ON PLATFORM NUMBER 3.

COME ON, SIR. QUICK!

HEY!

SUPPANDI! ARE YOU TRYING TO KILL ME?

NO, NO, SIR…

… THERE'S A TRAIN COMING ON PLATFORM NUMBER 3. WON'T IT BE SAFER TO STAND ON THE TRACKS?

SHEESH!

IN PLACE

SUPPANDI HAD JUST COME IN AFTER SHOPPING FOR VEGETABLES.

SUPPANDI, COME HERE AND HELP ME FIX THIS NAIL.

PHEW! IT'S HOT OUTSIDE.

A SHORT WHILE LATER –

MUST YOU LEAVE THE VEGETABLES LYING AROUND? GO AND KEEP THEM IN THEIR PLACE.

YES, MA'AM.

?

ZIP

SOON –

WHERE DID YOU TAKE THE VEGETABLES, SUPPANDI?

TO THE VEGETABLE MARKET.

WHY?

YOU ASKED ME TO KEEP THEM IN THEIR PLACE. THAT IS THE PLACE I BROUGHT THEM FROM.

!

45

PRESCRIPTION FOLLOWED

AT THE DOCTOR'S CLINIC –

OOH! DOCTOR, WHEN WILL THIS STOMACH ACHE GO?

DON'T WORRY, SUPPANDI, JUST FOLLOW THIS PRESCRIPTION AND YOU WILL GET QUICK RELIEF.

AS SUPPANDI STEPPED OUT INTO THE WAITING ROOM OF THE CLINIC...

... A GUST OF WIND BLEW THE PRESCRIPTION OUT OF THE FIRST-FLOOR WINDOW.

HEY! WAIT!

NEXT DAY –

GOOD HEAVENS, SUPPANDI! HOW DID YOU HURT YOURSELF?

DOCTOR, DIDN'T YOU TELL ME TO FOLLOW THE PRESCRIPTION?

THAT'S RIGHT!

THE PRESCRIPTION FLEW OUT OF THE WINDOW AND I FOLLOWED IT.

CANDLES ARE FOR BURNING!

SUPPANDI'S EMPLOYER HAD BOUGHT A WATER FILTER –

WHAT IS THIS, SIR?

THIS IS A WATER FILTER, SUPPANDI.

AND WHAT ARE THESE?

THESE ARE THE FILTER CANDLES.

JUST THEN, THE LIGHTS WENT OUT –

OH NO! LIGHT SOME CANDLES QUICKLY.

YES, SIR.

WHAT IS THAT HORRIBLE SMELL?

WE'VE RUN OUT OF CANDLES, SIR.

...SO I LIT THE FILTER CANDLES INSTEAD.

AARGH!

ONE AND MANY

SUPPANDI BUYS A BOOK

HOW MUCH FOR THESE CHAPPALS?

90 RUPEES?

AND THESE?

110

I'LL TAKE THEM

WHY DID YOU TAKE THE MORE EXPENSIVE ONES, SIR?

IT'S BETTER TO PAY A LITTLE MORE AND GET A BETTER PRODUCT.

ER... SUPPANDI.

... GO TO THE BOOK SHOP AND GET ME THIS BOOK.

HOURS LATER –

HERE HE IS, AT LAST!

WHY DID YOU TAKE SO LONG? WASN'T THE BOOK AVAILABLE?

IT WAS. BUT THEY WERE ALL SELLING IT FOR NINE RUPEES.

I REMEMBERED WHAT YOU HAD TOLD ME... THAT IT WAS BETTER TO PAY A LITTLE MORE AND GET A BETTER PRODUCT. SO I WENT FROM SHOP TO SHOP TILL I FOUND ONE SELLING IT FOR THIRTEEN RUPEES.

SUPPANDI WELCOMES A GUEST

SUPPANDI'S EMPLOYER HAD GONE TO THE AIRPORT TO FETCH HIS BROTHER WHO WAS RETURNING FROM AMERICA AFTER FIFTEEN YEARS. AND IT HAPPENED TO BE THE DAY OF HOLI.

HOPE THEY DON'T THROW THAT COLOURED WATER ON ME.

DON'T WORRY!

I'LL GET YOU HOME SAFELY.

THERE! WE'RE HOME AND NOT A SPOT OF COLOUR ON YOU.

I CAN'T BELIEVE IT! THIS IS TOO GOOD TO BE TRUE.

YOU CAN STAY INDOORS THE REST OF THE DAY.

YOU WILL BE WELL LOOKED AFTER BY MY NEW SERVANT.

AH, THERE HE IS.

WELCOME, SIR!

ENJOY! IT'S HOLI.

EEEEEEESH!

NO COCONUTS

ONE DAY SUPPANDI AND HIS EMPLOYER WENT TO THE MARKET.

DO YOU WANT ANYTHING, SUPPANDI?

YES, SIR, I WANT TO EAT WHATEVER THAT HAWKER IS SELLING.

PANI PURI

YOU SHOULDN'T BUY EATABLES FROM THESE ROADSIDE HAWKERS. YOU COULD FALL SICK!

REALLY?

A FEW DAYS LATER, SUPPANDI'S EMPLOYER FELL ILL —

SUPPANDI, PLEASE GET ME SOME TENDER COCONUTS FROM THE MARKET. I WANT TO DRINK COCONUT WATER.

AN HOUR LATER –
WHAT TOOK YOU SO LONG AND WHERE ARE THE COCONUTS?

I DIDN'T BUY ANY BECAUSE THEY WOULDN'T HAVE BEEN GOOD FOR YOU.

WHY?

ONLY THE ROADSIDE HAWKERS HAD COCONUTS AND DIDN'T YOU TELL ME NEVER TO BUY EATABLES FROM THEM?

DIAL 100

SUPPANDI'S NEW EMPLOYER WAS A RICH BUSINESSMAN. ONE NIGHT –

SUPPANDI, THERE'S A ROBBER IN THE HOUSE! DIAL 100.

100? OKAY SIR.

SOON THE POLICE WILL COME AND CATCH THIS RASCAL.

SEVERAL MINUTES LATER –

EH? HE IS LEAVING, AND SO IS ALL MY WEALTH!

HE IS GONE! I AM RUINED!

SUPPANDI, WHY HAVEN'T THE POLICE ARRIVED YET?

I THINK IT'S BECAUSE I HAVEN'T FINISHED DIALLING, SIR!

WHAT! WHY NOT?

YOU TOLD ME TO DIAL 100 AND I AM STILL AT EIGHTY-FOUR.

CLEANING UP

SUPPANDI, WHERE DID YOU TAKE THAT BANANA FROM?

YOU ASKED ME TO CLEAN OUT THE FRIDGE SIR, SO I DID THAT BY EATING UP ALL THE FOOD.

IDIOT! *GO AND POLISH THE FLOOR. I WANT IT CLEAN AND SHINING.*

Y...YES, SIR.

A LITTLE LATER –

YOU'VE DONE A *GOOD JOB,* SUPPANDI. THE FLOOR IS SPARKLING. WHAT DID YOU CLEAN IT WITH...?

...YAAARCH!

I USED YOUR HAIR OIL, SIR. YOUR HAIR ALWAYS LOOKS SO CLEAN AND SHINY AFTER YOU USE IT.

GRRR!

A FRUITY STORY

Once a play was staged in our school and I was asked to play the role of a fruit-seller. On the appointed day, I dressed myself in the fruit-seller's clothes, took a basketful of fruits and set off to school. I walked briskly for a while. But suddenly a boy came to me to buy a fruit. He thought that I was a real fruit-seller. I felt sorry for the little boy and gave him a fruit free of cost. He went away happily.

I walked on but then a number of boys gathered around me shouting, "I want a fruit! I want a fruit!". I told them that I was not a real fruit-seller but they would not listen. Then I learned that the boy to whom I had given the fruit had told them about my generosity. I had to give all of them a fruit each and soon my basket was empty. I walked on and reached the school. I narrated the incident to my teacher who had to buy me a bunch of bananas. I played the role of fruit-seller with gusto because I had already begun to feel like one!

A true-life incident sent by :
Mohd. Altaf Siah, Shrinagar
Kashmir – 191121.

IT HAPPENED TO ME...

THE REVENGE

One day, as usual, my friends and I went out to play cricket in the vacant space near my house. As always the tennis ball went into our neighbour's house. But I don't know what made him cut the ball that day. I suppose he was irritated and so was I.

The next day having decided to teach the man a lesson, we played with a cricket ball. In the very first over I hit it into my neighbour's house. I wanted to see what he would do as he certainly could not cut the hard ball.

There was no sound from his house and so we went in to get our ball. To our shock we found the man sitting quietly and bleeding from his head, where the ball had hit him. I apologised for what I had done and he generously forgave me.

A true life incident sent by:
K Krishna Murthy,
Mangalore – 575 004.

BOTH INCIDENTS ON THIS PAGE HAVE BEEN TAKEN FROM TINKLE ARCHIVES.

IT HAPPENED TO ME....

BLUNDERELLA

This incident happened on the annual day of our school. I was selected to play the role of 'Cinderella' in the play being staged. The chief guest was the education minister of our state. He, our principal and other teachers were sitting in the front row. The play went on smoothly till the scene, in which the clock strikes twelve and Cinderella rushes out of the hall, leaving her slippers behind. I began to run, trying to get the slippers off my feet but one of the slippers just wouldn't come off. At last I gave such a hard kick that the slipper flew and landed right on the chief guest's head. The audience burst into laughter and I rushed to the back of the stage.

A true-life incident
Sent by:
Miss H Ashwini,
Hyderabad – 500013

FLOATING GHOST

I woke up in the middle of the night and on looking out of the window saw a dreadful sight. There was something out there. It had hands and legs, but no head. Its palms and feet were also missing. It was hovering in the air, moving backwards and forwards.

Terrified, I pulled the sheet over my face. A little later I fell asleep. When I woke up I looked fearfully out of the window but there was nothing. I felt relieved. When I narrated the incident to my mother in trembling tones she burst out laughing.

I was annoyed and asked her why she was laughing. My mother explained that what I had seen at night was just my father's white kurta - pyjama which had been washed and hung out to dry.

A True-life Incident
Sent By:
Amit Sureka
Mumbai- 400092.

BOTH INCIDENTS ON THIS PAGE HAVE BEEN TAKEN FROM TINKLE ARCHIVES.

SUPPANDI
the spy

Writer: Luis

Illustrator: Harsho Mohan

Colourist: Umesh Sarode

MY FAMILY HAS HAD A LONG AND GLORIOUS HISTORY! LET ME TELL YOU ABOUT MY GREAT-GREAT-GREAT GRANDFATHER…

HE TOO WAS CALLED SUPPANDI! THIS IS HIS STORY…

1866. THE ENGLISH COMMANDER OF FORT MOON, NEAR DIGHA IS WORRIED –

I WISH WE KNEW HOW MANY REBELS ARE REALLY OUT THERE, MORTIMER!

ONE REPORT SAYS 300, WHILE ANOTHER SAYS THEIR NUMBER IS CLOSER TO 4000!

THE FACT IS WE CAN NO LONGER TRUST OUR SPIES, SIR. SOME OF THEM MIGHT BE WORKING FOR THE ENEMY!

WE NEED TO SEND OUT A MAN WHOM WE CAN DEPEND ON, SOMEONE WHOM NO ONE WOULD EVER SUSPECT OF BEING A SPY…

61

63

64

68

WAIT A MINUTE... THEY DON'T LOOK LIKE OUR GUYS... THEY LOOK LIKE...

DEMONS!

WE'RE BEING ATTACKED BY DEMONS!

RUN!

IN FORT MOON —

TAN TARA TANTARA...TANTARA...

TAN-TARA...RA...

THE BUGLE! WE'RE BEING ATTACKED!

CUNNING DEVILS! ATTACKING AT DAWN TO TAKE US BY SURPRISE!